A Hole Is To Dig

AND

Open House
For Butterflies

Two Classics by
Ruth Krauss and Maurice Sendak

BARNES
&NOBLE
BOOKS
NEW YORK

Reprinted by permission of HarperCollins Publishers

A Hole Is To Dig

A FIRST BOOK OF FIRST DEFINITIONS

Thanks to a number of children and teachers in the
Harriet Johnson Nursery School; and special thanks
to children in the Rowayton School Kindergarten,
and their teacher, Harriet S. Sherman.

LC Number: 52-7731
ISBN 0-06-023405-9
ISBN 0-06-023406-7 (lib. bdg.)
ISBN 0-06-443205-X (pbk.)
First Harper Trophy edition, 1989.

Mashed potatoes are to
give everybody enough

A face is so you can make faces

A face is something to have
on the front of your head

Dogs are to kiss people

Hands are to hold

A hand is to
hold up when
you want your turn

A hole is to dig

The ground is
to make a garden

Grass is to cut

Grass is to have on
the ground with dirt under it
and clover in it

Maybe you
could hide things
in a hole

A party is to say how-do-you-do
and shake hands

A party is to make
little children happy

Arms are to hug with

Toes are to wiggle

Ears are to wiggle

Mud is to jump in and slide in and
yell doodleedoodleedoo

Anh-h-h-h!

Doodleedoodleedoo-oo!

A castle is to build
in the sand

A hole is to sit in

A dream is to look at the night
and see things

Snow is to roll in

Buttons are to
keep people warm

The world is so
you have something
to stand on

The sun is to tell you when
it's every day

When you make your bed
you get a star

Grr-r-r

Little stones are for little children
to gather up and put in little piles

Oo! A rock
is when you trip on it
you should have watched where
you were going

Children are to love

A brother is to help you

A principal
is to take out
splinters

A mountain is to go to the top

A mountain is
to go to the bottom

A lap is so you
don't get crumbs
on the floor

A mustache is to
wear on Halloween

A hat is to wear on a train

Toes are to dance on

Eyebrows are to
go over your eyes

A sea shell is to hear the sea

A wave is to wave bye-bye

Big shells are to put
little shells in

A hole is to plant a flower

A watch is to hear it tick

Dishes are to do

Cats are so you can have kittens

Mice are to
eat your cheese

Noses are to rub

A nose is to blow

A match is to blow

A whistle is to make people jump

Rugs are so you don't get splinters in you

Boodlyboodlyboodly

A floor is so you
don't fall in the hole
your house is in

Hunh! Rugs are so
dogs have napkins

A hole is
for a mouse
to live in

A door is to open

A door is to shut

A hole is
to look through

Steps are to sit on

A hole is
when you step in it
you go down

Hands are to make things

Hands are to eat with

A tablespoon is to eat a table with

A package is to look inside

The sun is so it can be a great day

A book
is to look at

Open House
for Butterflies

A screaming song is good to
know in case you need to scream

A good thing to think about is
what kind of face to make when
you say please

If you're a horse
a good thing to
think about is
a castle of sugar lumps

You should make a sad face
when you meet a crocodile

A baby is very convenient to be

Open house for butterflies
is a good thing to have

Look

 Look

Look

Look

Look

Look

Look! I'm running away with my imagination

Lapkin is a good word to know

Nojuice is a good word to know
in case you have a glass of no juice

Dogdog is a good word to know in case you
see a dog and you see it in a looking glass too

I have a two-wheeler

I have a three-wheeler

I have a broken-wheeler

Broken-wheeler is a good word to know

There should be a parade
when a baby is born

A baby is so you
could be the boss

A good way to tell it's snowing is when everybody runs outside and throws their hats in the air

The minute you meet some people
you know you will hate their mothers

Lovabye is a good word to know

Suppose
old people
grew down as
young people
grew up

A good way to get yourself to go to bed
is yell **All aboard for bed!**

I always go to bed
after my bedtime

When you're very very tired just
throw your tired away

Pink means nightie

Easter eggs are all different outside
but they're all alike inside

Can a
bride fly?

A wedding song is good to
know in case you're at a wedding

icky goo
icky goo
icky goo
goo goo

A work song for clay is good to know

I made a little
clay ball and
threw it hard
and it got flat
and now I have a flat ball

bump

bump

bumpety

A song for bumpy roads is good to know

A good thing to know is what a punch in
the nose feels like in case somebody asks

Do you want a punch in the nose?

A baby makes the mother
and father—otherwise they're
just plain people

Yesterday shows another day is here

  Are you pretending
you're really a lion?

If you're pretending you're a
lion it's good to know if you're
pretending you're really a lion

Remember the day we
went to the city? No

If you went out and forgot your
pretend friends where would you
go when you went back for them?

—the day we went
to see the tall
buildings—

No

—the day we
went on
the train—

Oh! You mean the
day the
elephant
climbed
the tree

A good thing
to know is this road
is private for everybody

A good thing
not to be is
a plant because someone might think
you are a weed and pull you up by the roots

I wouldn't
want to be
an apple

A queen suit is a good thing
to have in case you're planning
to be a queen when you grow up

A little tree is a good thing not to be because
you might grow up to be a telephone pole

Can a caboose
grow up?

Big shows you grew

Marriage is so your brothers and sisters
should grow up and get married and
then you could be the only child

Grownup means
to go to nursery
school

Everybody should be quiet
near a little stream and listen

A bowl of milk is a good thing to take along
in case you're pretending you're a kitten

I like little thunder

One thing no good about a big brother is
when you hit him he hits you right back

Yanh yanh yanh!
I don't have a
little red wagon
and you do

You can always boast you **don't** have it

What would
happen if I
didn't dot
the i?

When you run out
of cereal can you
run into it again?

A good way to make an Indian hat is cut a picket fence out of
paper and put the ends together and you'll have an Indian hat

There are all kinds of ears
in this world

A nose is to be
nosey with

Pins never unfit you
you can wear them your whole life

A baby dances with its feet in the air

If I had a tail I'd pull my wagon
with it while I was picking flowers

If I had a tail
I wouldn't be a lion
I might eat too many
people and then I'd get sick

If I had a tail I'd give it to someone who needs it

I think a race looks
prettier when
everybody comes
in even

A good way to end a story is

The prince and the princess lived happy ever
after and the mice lived happy ever after too